Getting Around

By Car

Cassie Mayer

www.heinemann.co.uk/library
Visit our website to find out more information about **Heinemann Library** books.

To order:
☎ Phone 44 (0) 1865 888066
▤ Send a fax to 44 (0) 1865 314091
▭ Visit the Heinemann Bookshop at www.heinemann.co.uk/library to browse our catalogue and order online.

First published in Great Britain by Heinemann Library, Halley Court, Jordan Hill, Oxford OX2 8EJ, part of Harcourt Education. Heinemann is a registered trademark of Harcourt Education Ltd.

© Harcourt Education Ltd 2006.
First published in paperback in 2007.
The moral right of the proprietor has been asserted.

Editorial: Tracey Crawford, Cassie Mayer, Daniel Nunn, and Sarah Chappelow
Design: Jo Hinton-Malivoire
Picture Research: Tracy Cummins
Production: Duncan Gilbert

Originated by Chroma Graphics (Overseas) Pte. Ltd
Printed and bound in China by South China Printing Company

13 digit ISBN 978 0 431 18218 6 (hardback)

11 10 09 08 07 06
10 9 8 7 6 5 4 3 2 1

13 digit ISBN 978 0 431 18322 0 (paperback)

11 10 09 08 07
10 9 8 7 6 5 4 3 2 1

British Library Cataloguing in Publication Data
Mayer, Cassie
Getting around by car
1.Automobile travel - Juvenile literature 2.Roads - Juvenile literature
I.Title
388.3'42

Acknowledgements
The publishers would like to thank the following for permission to reproduce photographs:
Alamy pp. **7** (Transtock Inc.), **13** (Andre Jenny), **15** (Carphotos), **22** (Motoring Picture), **23** (Transtock Inc); Corbis pp. **4** (G. Boutin/zefa), **5** (Reuters), **10** (Douglas Kirkland), **11** (Bo Zaunders), **12** (Sygma), **14** (Michael Kim), **18** (Manfred Mehlig/zefa), **19** (Pete Saloutos), **20** (Joel W. Rogers), **21** (Joson/zefa); Getty Images pp. **6** (Adams), **8** (Hall), **9** (McLain), **16** (IPS), **17** (Johner).

Cover image of a car in Cuba reproduced with permission of Bob Krist/Corbis. Backcover image of a Volkswagen Beetle reproduced with permission of Reuters/Corbis.

Every effort has been made to contact copyright holders of any material reproduced in this book. Any omissions will be rectified in subsequent printings if notice is given to the publishers.

The paper used to print this book comes from sustainable resources.

Contents

Getting around by car

Every day people move from place to place.

Some people move by car.

How cars move

wheel

Cars have wheels to help them move.

engine

Cars have engines to help them move.

smooth road

Cars go on smooth roads.

Cars go on rough roads.

Types of cars

Some cars are big.

Some cars are small.

Some cars are long.

Some cars are short.

Some cars are fast.

Some cars are slow.

Where cars go

Cars go through cities.

Cars go through the country.

Some cars can go through deserts.

Some cars can go through forests.

Cars can take you to many places.

And your feet can do the rest.

Car vocabulary

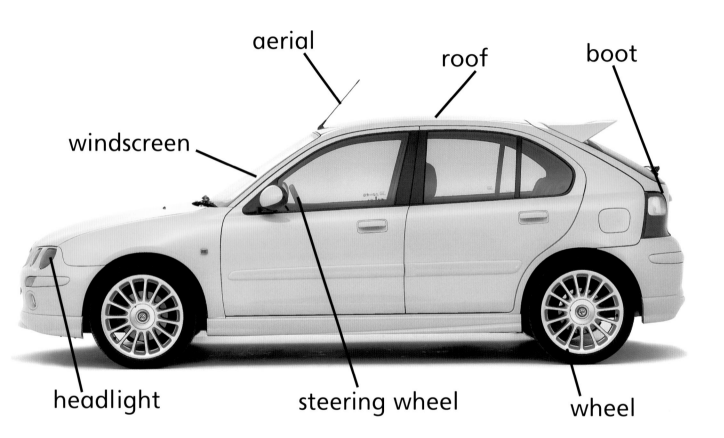

aerial

roof

boot

windscreen

headlight

steering wheel

wheel

Picture glossary

engine a machine that makes a car move

Index

Notes to Parents and Teachers
Before reading
Talk about going on a car journey. Where did they go? Where did they sit? What did they see?
Talk about the engine, the wheels, the steering wheel, windscreen wipers, and the boot.
Talk about different makes of cars. Which car do they like best?

After reading
Make a simple model of a car using building bricks or boxes.
Cut out pictures of cars from magazines and help the children to label them (windscreen, boot, wheels etc.) Display the collage on the wall.
Tell the children to move in different ways: jerkily like an old car; smoothly like a family car; fast like a sports car.
To the tune of "The Farmer's in his Den" sing and do the actions to the song "I'm driving my big fast car/my little old car/my smart, long car/ my very short car." For the third line sing "Toot, toot, toot, toot" and repeat the first line.